GILES

Sunday Express
&
DAILY EXPRESS
CARTOONS

FIFTIETH SERIES

GILES CHARACTERS ™ & © 1996 Express Newspapers plc.
Published by

Pedigree®
BOOKS

The Old Rectory, Matford Lane, Exeter, Devon, EX2 4PS
Under licence from Express Newspapers plc.
Printed in Italy. ISBN 1-874507-65-1

£6.99

GI 50

Foreword by
HRH
The Prince of Wales

ST. JAMES'S PALACE

It is an enormous sadness that, with the death of Carl Giles in 1995, this will be the last traditional Giles Annual to be published.

For countless people who, like myself, have grown up in Britain since the Second World War, "Giles" has been a much loved "institution". I myself always looked forward to his cartoons. Somehow they captured almost unerringly the mood of the nation. His gently wicked, yet never vindictive, humour, wherever it was applied - to politics, my family, the day-to-day incidents and dramas of life in Britain and abroad - endeared him to all of us in a way that no other cartoonist has achieved this century.

In this 50th commemorative year, Giles' humour still represents in so many ways the best of our nation's character: an ability never to take ourselves too seriously, coupled with the courage to poke fun and to take a stand against injustice from whatever source.

Carl Giles will be missed by many people, both in Britain and overseas, but his ability to distill and to civilise the essence of our world with his humour will live on.

Charles

CONTENTS

Foreword by

HRH Prince of Wales

1967 – 1976
1977 – 1986
1987 – 1996

For over half a century, the cartoons of Giles have been a quintessential aspect of British public life. As a commentator on the life of this country, with his unique blend of draughtsmanship, observation, dark humour and affection, he has never been equalled.

"Carl" Ronald Giles was born in 1916 in Islington. He received no formal training as an artist, but found work after leaving school at 14, first in an animation studio and latterly as a cartoonist for Reynold's News. His first cartoon for the Express appeared in October 1943, and in August two years later, he debuted his 'cartoon family' who would become the enduring mainstay of his work. Even by the end of the war he had become a beloved national figure thanks to his morale-lifting creations. Throughout his career, his work was published twice a week in the Daily Express and once a week in the Sunday Express.

Giles affectionately chronicled in the suburban life of Middle England, with cherished subjects like public health and transport, education, farming, and the recreational habits of the middle classes including his own beloved boating, and favourite targets like petty bureaucracy and arch pomposity recur across the years.

1947 – 1956

Giles had already captured the spirit of the War itself as a War Correspondent Cartoonist, and now he turned his attention from his patriotic wartime work to observing Britain's peacetime recovery and her struggle through the austerity of shortages, rationing and rebuilding. In many respects, he boosted public morale as much after the War as during it. His cartoons provided a cheerful, encouraging commentary during the bleak post-war years, simultaneously railing at the state of the nation and smiling through those lean times just the same. Giles lived on a working farm, and the concerns of the rural communities were therefore very close to his heart, particularly when politics impinged on them, as can be seen from the cartoon of October 11th, 1953.

1979

"A very remarkable impersonation, Wilmot – now if you'll kindly put my hat back where you found it, and bring the cane over here ..."

Daily Express, September 23rd, 1952

"The manager says he'll be my Valentine if I drop that left-wing-bolshie shop steward, and the shop steward says he'll be my Valentine if I drop that right-wing-capitalist beast of a manager."

Daily Express, February 14th, 1950

Snow fell in Egypt this week.

Daily Express, February 10th, 1950

"Ho, no – the village girls weren't good enough for him – HE was going to marry Gorgeous Gussie when HE grew up."

Daily Express, January 24th, 1950

"Goodbye, and don't forget – next holiday you bring the Coronation Stone and we'll get you a couple of salmon."

Daily Express, September 15th, 1954

"We're just teaching him a know a Whitehall land requisitioner when he sees one."

Sunday Express, July 25th, 1954

"That's a nice thing to call a baby on the first day of National Baby Week."

Sunday Express, June 13th, 1954

"Blackpool's got everything t' Festival's got, lad – except one o' those things where you all get struck by lightning if you're underneath."

Daily Express, May 24th, 1951

"This story about a woman pilot in Korea has started something."

Daily Express, January 30th, 1951

"Dad – he's pinching our coal."

Sunday Express, December 24th, 1950

"We've gone to all this trouble and now you've decided you don't *want* to go to the moon after all."

Sunday Express, November 5th, 1950

"When tea comes off the ration next week I suppose we'll be losing old Hot-and-strong and
Weak-and-milky."

Daily Express, October 3rd, 1952

"I'd cut girls right out of my life rather than go all round Britain on a ——— bicycle to get 'em."

Daily Express, September 8th, 1952

"Just think, Mummy, when Spike and I are married, you'll be able to come and visit us in
New York two or three times a week."

Daily Express, August 28th, 1952

"That candidate who kissed my baby last week must have lost his deposit – he just gave baby a whack with his umbrella."

Sunday Express, October 28th, 1951

"Stroking my bull and calling him 'a dear old horse' don't give me a lot of
confidence in your knowledge of agriculture."

Daily Express, October 11th, 1953

"I'm off duty in ten minutes, when I shall show Davy Crockett here who's King of the Wild Frontier."

Sunday Express, May 20th, 1956

"Pass on, Sweetie – I've put my sixpence in your money-box."

Daily Express, July 6th, 1958

"Hey you! Put that cap straight. Third man there – get your hair fixed.
Marilyn will be passing this way any minute."

Sunday Express, July 15th, 1956

"My Harry's a striker on holiday – the other one's his boss who happens to be staying at our hotel."

Daily Express, July 29th, 1956

"Good old Nasser."

Daily Express, July 31st, 1956

"Giving me a cup with no handle and saying 'I hope it chokes you, you blacklegging old scab'
ain't forgiving and forgetting, Miss."

Daily Express, August 14th, 1956

"British Air Ministry? You know those three girl diplomats you sent to encourage G.I.s to like Britain? Well, they've married three G.I.s and gone to live in the States."

Sunday Express, October 24th, 1954

"Grandma can't find her Sunday dress – what was the Guy Fawkes you burnt on Friday wearing at the time?"

Sunday Express, November 7th, 1954

"Careful, George, your little brother is watching you."

Daily Express, December 16th, 1954

Dedicated to all those compelled to spend Christmas in hospital, where there is little or no escape from giving a hand with the decorations. I know, I've had some.

Daily Express, December 24th, 1954

1957 – 1966

By the late fifties, Giles's cast of characters were firmly established, and he was busy recording the fast changing modern world. The beginnings of the space race, rock and roll and the technological revolution intruded upon the suburban world of the cartoons as they did in life itself: gently, distantly and obliquely. More often than not, they were also greeted with suspicion and scorn. The cartoon of July 6th, 1958 perfectly illustrates the withering disdain the Giles family held for world events beyond their garden fence. Despite the appealing and often tranquil world Giles portrayed, he could still be bitter and acid. It is significant that Giles's greatest creation was the formidable and single-minded Grandma, scourge of the family and the suburban world that orbited around her. Like Giles himself, Grandma took the Sport of Kings very seriously; witness the cartoon from March 22nd, 1960.

Here too, we see Chalkie, the wonderfully malevolent schoolmaster character who Giles based upon a spectre from his own school days. Gaunt and predatory, Chalkie was also woundingly acerbic and unfailingly wise.

Several cartoons in this period also reflect Giles's sidelong glance at the vagaries of fashion, particularly the more extreme samples that decorated an increasingly permissive age.

Giles received an OBE 1959.

1986

"When a poor man came in sight ... Gathering winter fu-el."

Daily Express, December 6th, 1956

"Who's been playing blocking canals and sinking ships in my bath?"

Sunday Express, November 18th, 1956

"These yours? We found them stowed away in the Trans-Antarctic expedition ship."

Daily Express, November 15th, 1956

"BALL BOY!"

Sunday Express, June 27th, 1965

"I don't think Henry was wise to say now they've got extra pay he will expect extra service."

Sunday Express, June 13th, 1965

"Mr President? I guess they've sure set the pace this time."

Daily Express, June 10th, 1965

"Never mind what they said in Parliament yesterday about the arts being a vital element in our whole standard of living, my lady."

Daily Express, April 29th, 1965

"Good heavens no. she's wearing one of these new mini-dresses."

Daily Express, June 14th, 1966

"O.K., girls, by the left, quick march! We'll give 'em new-look uniforms for the Scouts."

Sunday Express, June 12th, 1966

"I thought I told you to stay out of sight while the judges were around."

Sunday Express, February 10th, 1957

"We won't detain you long, Miss Keeler. Just until all the American V.I.P.s are out of the country."

Sunday Express, June 30th, 1963

"Grandma says we'll all look silly sitting on a cloud playing harps with our heads off telling one another that the threat
to drop an atom bomb was a hoax."

Sunday Express, July 6th, 1958

"Remember you said 'If it's O.K. for the Duke to break an appointment to play polo,
Chalky can't say anything if we break an appointment to go fishing?"

Daily Express, July 1st, 1958

"Sir! They keep giving me wolf-whistles."

Daily Express, May 22nd, 1958

"Bert, I don't want to depress you but your governor's just bought one of those new tractors that don't need a driver."

Daily Express, July 7th, 1964

"Jones will probably do better next round if he drops this 'I'm-the-greatest-I'm-the-prettiest' technique."

Daily Express, February 27th, 1964

"I bet Ringo's dad didn't make him practise down the bottom of the garden."

Sunday Express, February 23rd, 1964

"One minute they tell us there won't be anybody around in 1999 ..."

Sunday Express, September 6th, 1959

"If the Summit talks fall through, calling him Dwight Nikita Harold is going to make him look pretty stupid."

Sunday Express, August 30th, 1959

"I'd like to get within catapult range of that school medical officer who says
there are too many Billy Bunters these days."

Daily Express, August 25th, 1959

"Next time your Dad pays you your fourpence pocket money by cheque you go get
your bulls' eyes somewhere else."

Daily Express, May 12th, 1959

"When those among us who failed to remember to put their clocks forward are comfortably seated I will continue."

Sunday Express, April 19th, 1959

"It was your idea that we share each other's interests, Mother – if *I* watched
two weeks of Wimbledon *you'd* take up golf."

Sunday Express, July 3rd, 1960

"Not too 'ard, Sarge. I'm playing the joanna at the Reefer and 'Emp club tonight."

Daily Express, April 26th, 1969

"Anybody here ride the last horse in the last race?"

Daily Express, March 22nd, 1960

"Next time you see a policeman following say 'Dad, here comes a policeman' not 'Dad, here come the Apaches.'"

Sunday Express, May 21st, 1961

"Good night, Elvis Presley, good night, Cliff Richard – come in, Yuri Gagarin."

Sunday Express, April 16th, 1961

"One thing's for sure – if you want to stay in the monkey business you want to drop that well-*I*-did-*my*-bit attitude while the colonel's around."

Daily Express, April 13th, 1961

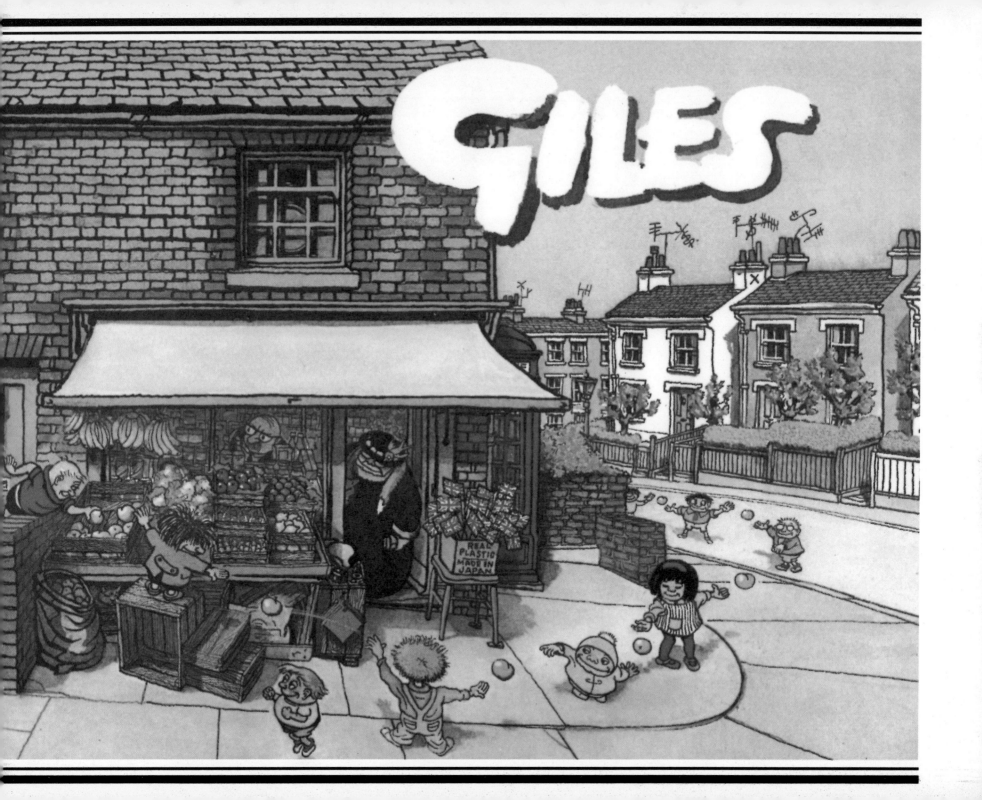

1967 – 1976

Mankind had reached the Moon, which gave Giles pause to reflect on mankind's relentlessly normal life back on Earth. A pair of cartoons here, just days apart in July 1969, show "Earth Man" as unwelcome at home as he is in the lunar landscape. The cares of Womankind also feature strongly in the early seventies. Giles traditionally gave the womenfolk of his world the controlling interest, but now he delighted in portraying the way sexual equality was puncturing the pompous bastions of masculinity. Aside from the delicious vulnerability of the December 29th, 1975 cartoon, Giles shows us men squirming in the face of female equality and falling foul of political correctness even as far back as January 5th, 1967.

However, Giles was nothing if not even handed and in his cartoon of May 18th, 1971 the culture clash of a suddenly mixed Jockey Club shows the behaviour of both sexes in a less than flattering light.

Another favourite subject that was visited several times in this period was the snobbery and pseudo-intellectualism of the art world. Giles meted out ruthless ridicule on art-pseuds, made all the more potent by the fact that the cartoons were so obviously the product of a greatly talented artists.

Giles's guerrilla war against the forces of officious bureaucracy was probably never waged with a more bleak and Orwellian touch than in his cartoon of February 6th, 1973. The pinstripe executioners are uniform and bland and the charge, in the light of grim pylons and masts that stretch away behind, ludicrous.

Giles's prediction that the standpipes from the long, hot summer of '76 would be around for a while to come was more a reflection of his opinion on government than on climate.

1988

"Look at it this way, lady—with a couple of these in your garden there's less chance of them turning your place into an airfield."

Sunday Express, May 14th, 1967

"Mum! Dad's 'If-they-tax-tobacco-again-I'm-definitely-giving-it-up' crisis is over."

Daily Express, March 21st, 1968

"There we are – and if I know anything about British Governments it will still be with you in 2076."

Daily Express, August 17th, 1976

"Think very carefully, sonny – are you absolutely sure that was the
man you saw using a hose on his window box?"

Sunday Express, April 11th, 1976

"Grandma, with a grave
international crisis over the future
of cod you're not
supposed to give yours to
the cat."

Daily Express, January 26th, 1976

"Come along, don't be shy – under the new Act there's not a scrap of difference between you and me."

Daily Express, December 29th, 1975

"That leaves you Butch or Grandma."

Sunday Express, August 10th, 1975

"What d'you mean 'Everyone will laugh at 'em'. May I ask just who the hell's going to see 'em?"

Daily Express, December 12th, 1974

"SHOW THAT TO LAUGHING BOY."

Daily Express, November 12th, 1974

"Stick this on, Vanessa, and let's have another go."

Sunday Express, April 30th, 1972

"Blast! They might give you a bit of warning when these power cuts end."

Daily Express, February 10th, 1972

"No sooner one war ends than another breaks out – go and tell the producer
we've got fresh trouble with Israel and the Arabs."

Sunday Express, December 19th, 1971

"Genuine Top of the Pops or not – thirty-three times without a break is enough."

Sunday Express, May 20th, 1973

"Go and tell dad Auntie Florrie's pup has just created a little work of art in the hall."

Sunday Express, October 17th, 1976

"I know I haven't got the hang of it yet – she's just charged me VAT."

Daily Express, April 3rd, 1973

"We, the Local Council, consider your application to build a kennel for your Fido
would constitute a violation of the rural charms of the area."

Daily Express, February 6th, 1973

"60% Pepsicola, 25% Candyfloss, 15% choc ice in charge of a donkey! Mrs. Castle won't like this."

Daily Express, October 3rd, 1967

"Will the gentleman who endowed the new biology mistress with the undesirable term 'Sex Kitten' kindly step out here."

Daily Express, January 5th, 1967

"One more won't do you any harm."

Sunday Express, December 11th, 1966

"The old folks are at home watching Alice in Wonderland."

Sunday Express, November 27th, 1966

"I want to phone my lawyers – he pulled my 'air."

Daily Express, August 26th, 1971

"Women jockeys! Won't race in my colours unless I find her a matching lipstick."

Daily Express, May 18th, 1971

"Damn flowers – never a bottle of Scotch."

Sunday Express, March 21st, 1971

"I'm not having a son
of mine christened Apollo
and that's final."

Daily Express, July 24th, 1969

"Kindly inform your mother that Earth Man is home and wants his tea."

Daily Express, July 17th, 1969

"Nice start, fellas."

Sunday Express, July 13th, 1969

"If we all watched where we were going instead of watching Sister Morgan's new uniform ..."

Daily Express, May 14th, 1970

"Pity. Vera's thrived on it all her life."

Daily Express, November 27th, 1969

1977 – 1986

In this selection, the stalwart themes of Giles's cartoon world are once more ably represented. The work also gains an additional topicality through the way Giles took his inspiration from the headlines of the day, however trivial.

Giles cartoons made many visits to both the Boat Show and the sea itself, often with majestically over-ambitions results. Here too are several fine examples of the wonderfully melancholy rain-slick station platforms and pavements where so many of Giles's cartoon moments occurred.

Giles's ability to impress us was mostly a result of the meticulous realism of his locations and his personae. Packed full of convincing detail and clutter, which often almost overwhelmed the central joke, his work could never be described as simply caricature or satire. Giles extensively researched his settings and backgrounds, often drawing from life. He toured the country in a studio caravan that he had himself purpose-built, building up reference sketches for his work. His formative experiences as an animator in the studios of Sir Alexander Korda in the 1930s also shines through on many occasions. His cartoons often seem to be in motion, and he manages to convey a sense of sequence, of cause and effect. See, for example, the cartoon of October 14th, 1980.

1987

"I'll do my best not to win, but if I lose I'll knock the stuffing out of you."

(Headline: Head bans competition in school)

Sunday Express, July 13th, 1986

"Far enough, Adonis."

Sunday Express, August 12th, 1979

"Vera – if I've got any tears to shed this morning I give you my written guarantee right now they're not for E.T."

Daily Express, December 9th, 1982

"Who the 'ell's been sleeping in my bed?" said Father Bear; "That bleeding little nymphomanic, Goldie Locks," wagered Mummy Bear. "Why, the two-timing, double-crossing no-good," murmured Baby Bear. Then they all

(There was an uproar in the Commons about cleaning up children's TV)

Daily Express, December 2nd, 1982

"Did you read about that customer who left a waitress £162,000?"

Sunday Express, October 23rd, 1983

"They gave Fred an alarm clock to wake him up to let him know he's arrived."

(For better timekeeping, BR presented free watches to staff)

Sunday Express, January 8th, 1984

"Apart from trading without a licence to sell – I'm checking if bathwater can be sold on Sundays."

(Headline: Americans queue to buy Royal bathwater)

Sunday Express, November 10th, 1985

"Off you go and rejoice – and steer clear of the Falklands 200 mile restricted zone."

Daily Express, May 2nd, 1982

"I reckon she heard you say 'Hear, hear' to Ted's speech at Blackpool"

Daily Express, October 20th, 1981

"Excuse me, Sir"

(Whitehall begins biggest mole hunt)

Daily Express, October 28th, 1980

Angela Rippon says she often feels like saying it, Sir!"

(There are times when I want to say sod it . . . Angela Rippon)

"I'll bet the Royal Grandma doesn't start her birthday celebrations with a large Guiness for breakfast"

Daily Express, July 15th, 1980

"If we're going to have this performance every time you canvass the discos
we're going to forget capturing the younger votes, my boy."

Daily Express, April 17th, 1979

"One day someone's going to crown this Egon Ronay."

Daily Express, November 7th, 1978

"Most of them start: 'Went to the seaside, smashing punch-up with the Old Bill'."

Daily Express, September 6th, 1983

"Dad, I've just counted up – we've got six more people than we've got in the family"

Daily Express, February 1st, 1983

"You say the lady kissed your head under the mistletoe thereby causing you sexual harassment?"

Daily Express, December 21st, 1982

"Blame TV sex for him asking you for a date – and Minder for the thump on the nose when you turned him down."

Daily Express, June 23rd, 1983

"That one doesn't need to dress up for Halloween."

Daily Express, October 31st, 1985

"Up since five cutting sandwiches for a picnic – what's the betting they're all back for lunch?"

Daily Express, May 27th, 1986

"Frank's little joke – 'For not wearing a seat belt it is the duty of this court to send you to a place where you will be hanged by the neck until you are dead."

Sunday Express, September 14th, 1986

"The Mary Rose woodwork being in good order after 437 years under water we may assume your coffee table has a lifespan of 10 minutes"

Daily Express, October 12th, 1982

"It's not Black Rod, M'Lord – the lady has left her box of Persil just behind the Throne."

Daily Express, January 22nd, 1985

"Hurricane Higgins got a black eye falling off a horse – I got mine when my wife saw me looking at THAT!"

Daily Express, January 7th, 1986

"I know they haven't got a sale on – that's one of my boy's Christmas presents going back the moment they open."

Daily Express, December 27th, 1984

"Well that should put paid to the legend of Father Christmas."

Daily Express, December 24th, 1984

"Agreed 100 per cent! We ask our brothers in the power stations not to have electricity cuts during the Muppet Show."

Daily Express, November 2nd, 1977

"I shouldn't put that one in, Sir – that's Mr. Wilmot, the maths master."

Daily Express, October 28th, 1977

1987 – 1996

The last decade of Giles's career was marred by ill-health, and he did not produce his cartoons at quite the prodigious rate of old. But the observation and the quality was still there, as were all the beloved characters: Mum and Dad, the hypochondriac Vera, the twins, Butch the dog, the unspeakably mature Ernie, Chalkie, and Stinker, the troll-like child most often seen with a camera, recording the day's disaster. And naturally, there was always Grandma.

When Giles died in August 1995, at his home in Witnesham, the nation rightly mourned the loss of a national treasure. But he had made his little family immortal.

And they, of course, had returned the favour.

1983

"Don't let 'me soften you up, Mac – get in there and give the umpires hell"

Daily Express, June 21st, 1988

"Don't blame us – it's your damn Grandma making the landlady open every tin and food packet
in the kitchen for inspection."

(Headline: Salmonella & listeria had been discovered in packed foods)

"It's the only arithmetic they know."

Daily Express, May 3rd, 1988

"Worse than getting the children back to school – getting him back to the Commons the morning after he has voted against Maggie."

Daily Express, April 19th, 1988

"I'd gladly give up decorating the living room so Vera could have her new gold tooth."

Sunday Express, January 21st, 1988

"Ahoy, there, I hope you haven't forgotten you're taking us all to the preview of the Boat Show today."

Daily Express, January 5th, 1988

"Florence, we appreciate your enthusiasm – and are aware that footballers advertise on their shirts . . ."

Daily Express, December 8th, 1987

"We sure got sex-equality in this house – he's switched the washing machine on and lifted the ironing board from the cupboard all on his own."

(Footnote: 'Idle' men still rule the roost)

Daily Express, November 17th, 1987

"Grandma, we don't mind you helping the neighbours clear up their hurricane damage for a fiver, but we do mind you sweeping it into our garden."

Daily Express, October 20th, 1987

"If we're going to bring you hours and hours of Miss World, someone's got to pay for it."

Daily Express, October 29th, 1987

"Don't get caught on the baby's age this time dear – just say 'Under 21'."

Daily Express, October 6th, 1988

(Headline: Fergie forgets Baby Bea's age.)

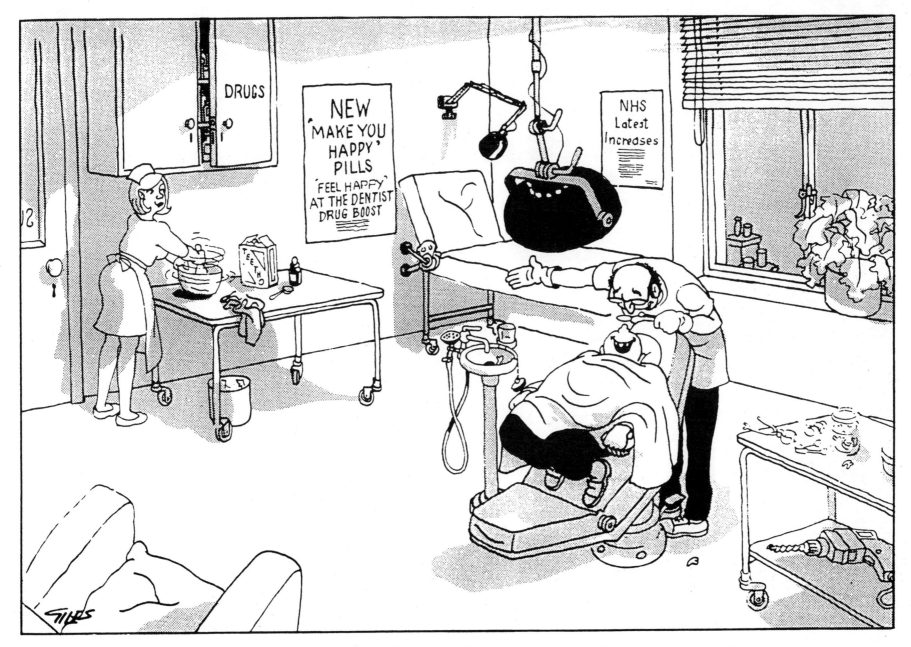

"Nurse, he'll need another couple of laughing pills – I think I've taken all the wrong ones out"

Daily Express, November 3rd, 1988

"How many times must I tell you: 'Is not Noddy the most stupid ...... you ever saw?' NOT 'Aint Noddy the most stupid ...... you ever saw?'"

Daily Express, November 17th, 1988

"I can see the headline, Vera – 'Amorous GP tells sexy patient to take her hat off'."

(Headline : Naked GP's surgery sex-romps taped)

Sunday Express, March 6th, 1988

"Went head over heels giving One an extra special curtsy"

(Headline: Prince Charles had another operation on his broken arm.)

"Remember me? I got three years for helping you with your enquiries."

(Headline: Police replace prison officers.)

Daily Express, February 2nd, 1989

"We are a Grandmother', but I don't think 'we' are amused."

(Headline: Mrs. Thatcher announces "We are a Grandmother".)

Sunday Express, March 5th, 1989

"Wakey, wakey – the lady's little boys can't get their Garfield and Odie suits off."

(Headline: 'Junior Doctors overworked' say Junior Doctors.)

Daily Express, January 3rd, 1989

"You call our swinging sixties rubbish – we could have bought Woburn for what you have to pay for a bed-sit."

Daily Express, July 26th, 1988

"Not quite in the Duchess of Windsor bracket – I'll give you £1.50 for the lot."

Sunday Express, April 5th, 1987

"Get that thing our of here or you'll be the one with the tears my boy."

Daily Express, September 22nd, 1987

"Far corner, Martina Navratilova to serve – FORE"

Sunday Express, July 5th, 1987

"Thin as a rake – thick as a plank – Prince Charles is still lucky he saw her first!"

Daily Express, January 22nd, 1987

"If the French don't want our lamb why don't we tell them we won't let them have any?"

Sunday Express, April 7th, 1989

*"We hope you've enjoyed this
50th Giles Annual.
Look out next year – a new decade
of Giles begins!"*